THE THINGS THEY CARRIED

by
Tim O'Brien

Student Packet

Written by
Pat Watson

Edited by
Lyn M. Pfordresher

Contains masters for:

2	Prereading Activities
4	Vocabulary Activities
1	Study Guide (6 pages)
6	Literary Analysis Activities
3	Comprehension Activities
4	Unit Quizzes
2	Final Tests (2 levels)

PLUS Detailed Answer Key

Note
The Broadway Books paperback edition of the book, ©1990 by Tim O'Brien, published 1998, was used to prepare this guide. Page references may differ in other editions.

Please note: This novel deals with sensitive, mature issues. Part may contain profanity, sexual references, and/or descriptions of violence. Please assess the appropriateness of this book for the age level and maturity of your students prior to reading it with them.

ISBN 1-58130-797-7

To order, contact your local school
supply store, or—

Getting the "Lay of the Land"

Directions: Prepare for reading by answering the following short-answer questions.

1. Who is the author?

   _____

2. What does the title suggest to you about the book?

   _____

   _____

   _____

   _____

3. When was the book written?

   _____

4. How many pages are there in the book?

   _____

5. Thumb through the book. Read three pages—one from near the beginning, one from near the middle, and one from near the end. What predictions do you make about the book?

   _____

   _____

   _____

   _____

   _____

6. What does the cover suggest to you about the book?

   _____

   _____

   _____

   _____

Vietnam War

Directions: Complete the following chart based on your personal knowledge of the Vietnam War.

Rationale for U.S. involvement:

_____

_____

_____

_____

_____

Different reactions to the war:

_____

_____

_____

_____

_____

Movies I've seen or books I've read:

_____

_____

_____

_____

_____

Vietnam veterans I know:

_____

_____

_____

_____

_____

My personal feelings about war: _____

_____

_____

_____

_____

_____

_____

metabolism (2)	topography (5)	volition (15)	ambiguities (16)
encyst (20)	comport (25)	antipersonnel (36)	lethal (36)
amortizing (40)	liberal (42)	hawk (42)	eviscerated (42)
deferments (43)	pacifist (44)	schizophrenic (44)	acquiescence (45)
platitudes (45)	cryptic (49)	reticence (51)	impassive (60)

Directions: Match each vocabulary word with the word or phrase closest in meaning.

_____ 1. metabolism

_____ 2. topography

_____ 3. volition

_____ 4. ambiguities

_____ 5. encyst

_____ 6. comport

_____ 7. antipersonnel

_____ 8. lethal

_____ 9. amortizing

_____ 10. liberal

_____ 11. hawk

_____ 12. eviscerated

_____ 13. deferments

_____ 14. pacifist

_____ 15. schizophrenia

_____ 16. acquiescence

_____ 17. platitudes

_____ 18. cryptic

_____ 19. reticence

_____ 20. impassive

a. enclose

b. reducing debt

c. reserved

d. warmonger

e. deadly

f. choice

g. disemboweled

h. peace lover

i. mental conflict

j. ground

k. unmoved

l. diches

m. postponements

n. consent

o. conduct oneself

p. broad-minded

q. ambiguous

r. against enemy

s. chemical process

t. uncertainties

rectitude (68)	surreal (71)	napalm (75)	ordnance (75)
aesthetic (81)	anarchy (82)	trite (83)	adism (87)
mundane (89)	superlatives (90)	imprecision (99)	opaque (105)
digressions (107)	endorphins (114)	eccentricity (116)	talisman (118)
pagoda (119)	cadres (128)	piasters (129)	hamlet (135)

Directions: Fill in the blanks in the following sentences with the correct vocabulary word. Use each word only once.

1. O'Brien believes a bombing raid has the _____ purity of moral indifference.

2. When _____ are released in the brain, a person can exhibit extraordinary behavior.

3. People have a right to expect the nations' leaders to exhibit _____.

4. Those who get pleasure from hurting others are involved in _____.

5. _____ of infantrymen penetrate into enemy territory.

6. The _____ events of life often lead to boredom.

7. Many _____(s) were destroyed in Vietnam.

8. In a country torn apart by war, law often turns into _____.

9. In retrospect, many of the war scenes become _____ in the survivors' minds.

10. When listening to some of the war stories, it is important to separate the _____ from the truth.

11. Kiowa feels that establishing a fortress in a _____ is sacrilegious.

12. _____ was used to blow away trees in the mountains of Vietnam.

13. South Vietnamese used _____ to purchase various items.

14. Heavy smoke will form an _____ cover over the terrain.

15. A person's quirky behavior may seem like an _____ to others.

16. Infantrymen must carry heavy _____ into battle.

17. A _____ word or phrase becomes stale.

18. Speaking with _____ causes lack of trust in a person's words.

19. A rabbit's foot is a _____ for some people.

20. Inconsistencies and _____ in a story can cause the listener to lose his/her train of thought.

affluent (138)   valor (140)   irony (146)   catharsis (157)
metaphoric (159)   virtues (160)   anthology (160)   complicity (160)
latrine (166)   tactically (169)   elusive (170)   condolences (176)

Directions: Use words from the vocabulary list to complete the following analogies.

1. JOYFUL is to MELANCHOLY as COWARDICE is to_____.

2. SOLDIER is to INFANTRYMAN as PRIVY is to _____.

3. SERMONS is to HOMILIES as CONSOLATIONS is to _____.

4. OVERT is to COVERT as VICES is to _____.

5. MUSIC is to OPUS as PROSE is to _____.

6. CONTRADICTION is to PARADOX as INCONGRUITY is to _____.

7. DECEIT is to DUPLICITY as CONSPIRACY is to _____.

8. INNOCENT is to GUILTY as POOR is to _____.

9. VAGUELY is to OBSCURELY as STRATEGICALLY is to _____.

10. OBVIOUS is to OBSCURE as FORTHRIGHT is to _____.

11. SARCASM is to SATIRICAL as COMPARISON is to _____.

12. ENTERTAIN is to COMEDY as PURIFY is to _____.

7

Name _____

gangrene (190)	tempo (193)	tic (201)	levitate (202)
rapport (203)	coherence (209)	atrocity (209)	resonance (210)
inflection (212)	wistful (212)	lucid (214)	mutant (222) snipe
hunt (221)	protoplasm (221)	ghoulish (222)	chronologies (228)
illusion (230)	inert (232)	translucent (235)	blatant (239)

Directions: Your teacher will assign you one word from the list above. Turn to the page where the word appears in the novel and examine how it is used in context. Complete the word map for your word and explain the finished map to the class.

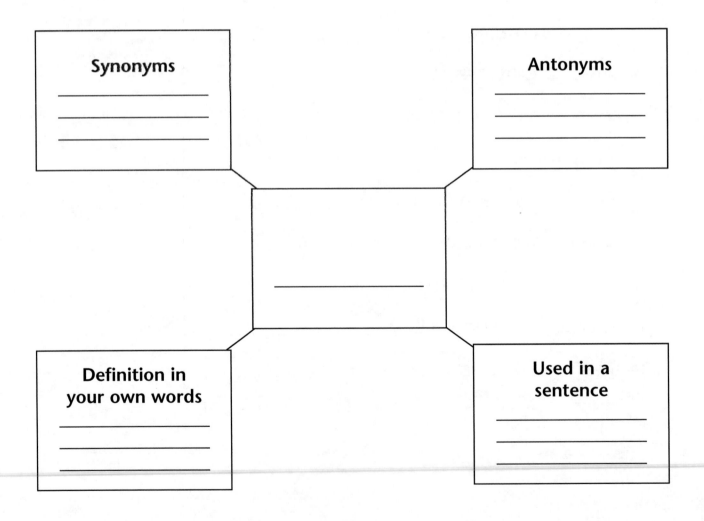

Name _____

Directions: Answer the following questions on a separate sheet of paper. Starred questions indicate thought or opinion questions or an activity. Use your answers in class discussions, for writing assignments, and to review for tests.

Patterns for poems in activities

Five-senses: Line 1—color of the emotion; Line 2—sound of the emotion; Line 3—taste of the emotion; Line 4—smell of the emotion; Line 5—sight (what the emotion looks like); Line 6—sensations evoked by the emotion

Metaphor/Simile: Line 1—noun (title); Lines 2–4—something about the subject, each line describing the subject in a different way; Line 5—a metaphor or simile that begins with the noun from line 1

Name Poem: Place the letters of the name vertically on the paper. Write a descriptive word or phrase beginning with each letter.

Diamente: Line 1—one word (a noun, the subject); Line 2—two words (adjectives that describe line 1); Line 3—three words ("-ing" or "-ed" words that relate to line 1); Line 4—four words (first two relate to line 1; second two relate to line 7); Line 5—three words ("-ing" or "-ed" words that relate to line 7); Line 6—two words (adjectives that describe line 7); Line 7—one word (noun that is the opposite of line 1)

Pages 1–26

1. Identify Lieutenant Jimmy Cross and explain what he carries into war (equipment, personal items, emotional burden).

2. *Who is Martha? What do you think she symbolizes to Lt. Cross?

3. *Why does Cross blame himself for Lavender's death? Explain why you do or do not think his guilt is justified.

4. Identify the men in Lt. Cross' platoon and identify some of the tangible and some of the intangible things they carry into war. What is their primary motivation for fighting in the war?

5. *Explain how the men in the platoon react to Lavender's death. Why do you think they react as they do?

6. Explain what is being compared in the metaphor, "...they dreamed of freedom birds." Why are these "birds" important to the men in Vietnam?

7. *Prediction: How many of the men in Cross' platoon will survive the war? Who do you think will survive?

8. *Activity: (a) Write a letter from Jimmy Cross to Martha after he burns her letters and pictures or (b) write a five-senses poem, "Guilt," reflecting Cross' reaction to Lavender's death.

9. *Activity: Begin a list of literary devices in the novel. Examples: Metaphor—Imagination: a killer; Simile—They moved like moles (p. 15).

Pages 27–38

1. *Why do you think O'Brien switches from third person to first person?

2. Who comes to visit O'Brien at his home in Massachusetts? What does this visit reveal about the two men?

3. *How does Jimmy Cross want to be remembered? Why do you think this is important to him?

4. *Identify two examples of terror and violence in the story "Spin." What do you think is the most poignant memory? Why?

5. *Identify two examples of sweetness and gentleness in the story "Spin." Which do you find the most touching? Why?

6. *Activity: Write a metaphor or simile poem based on the statement, "Stories are for eternity."

7. *Activity: Add two similes and one metaphor from this section to your list of literary devices. See pp. 34, 33, 34, 37.

Pages 39–66

1. Why hasn't O'Brien ever told the story "On the Rainy River"? Why does he decide to do so now?

2. How does O'Brien feel when his draft notice arrives in 1968? What does O'Brien discover about himself?

3. Explain O'Brien's reaction to the Vietnam War before and after his draft notice arrives.

4. *Describe O'Brien's summer job. Why do you think he gives such a graphic description of his work?

5. What options did those of draft age have during the Vietnam War? What is the only option that is feasible for O'Brien? Why?

6. What does O'Brien decide to do? Explain his emotional conflict over this decision. How does he react physically? mentally?

7. Who is Elroy Berdahl? Why is he influential in O'Brien's life?

8. *What does O'Brien decide to do about fleeing to Canada? Explain his moral dilemma and why he makes this choice. Explain why you do or do not think he made the right decision.

9. *Why do Lee Strunk and Dave Jenson fight? What is the result? What do you think this conflict reveals about men in war?

10. *Activity: (a) Write a poem beginning with "I stood at the crossroads..." or (b) a short essay in which you support or refute the statement beginning, "Courage comes to us in finite quantities..." (p. 40).

11. *Activity: Add three similes to your list. See pp. 43, 44, 47, 48, 54, 57, 60.

Pages 67–88

1. Identify three criteria O'Brien believes create a true war story.

2. *Explain why you do or do not think the stories Kiley and Sanders tell fit these criteria.

3. *How does Curt Lemon die? Why do you think O'Brien says this story "makes his stomach believe"?

4. *What happens to the water buffalo after Lemon's death? Why do you think the men react as they do?

5. *Explain why you think O'Brien calls Vietnam the "Garden of Evil."

6. Identify three contradictions O'Brien presents about war.

7. How does Curt Lemon react when he goes to the dentist? Why does he have the dentist pull a healthy tooth?

8. *Activity: (a) Write a name poem for Curt Lemon or (b) write a poem beginning with the phrase, "War is hell..."

9. *Activity: Add one simile and two metaphors to your list. See pp. 77, 78, 80.

Pages 89–116

1. *Identify Mary Anne Bell and Mark Fossie. Why does Mary Anne come to Vietnam? Explain why you do or do not think her arrival is believable.

2. Identify three ways in which Mary Anne changes after arriving in Vietnam.

3. What does Mark discover about Mary Anne's nighttime disappearances?

4. What eventually happens to Mary Anne?

5. *What do you think Mary Anne's transformation symbolizes? Explain your answer.

6. *Explain your interpretation of the metaphors on page 107: military forces—zoo; soldiers—animals.

7. *Activity: (a) Draw a caricature of Mary Anne as a combat-ready bride or (b) write two name poems for Mary Anne Bell, one before and one after her transformation.

8. *Add three similes and two metaphors to your list. See pp. 92, 93, 96, 105, 107, 109, 111.

Pages 117–136

1. Why do you think "Stockings" follows Mary Anne's story?

2. What is Henry Dobbins' good-luck charm? What does this symbolize to him?

3. How does Kiowa feel about establishing a fortress at the pagoda?

4. *Explain why you think the monks keep going through the motions of washing their hands.

5. *What does O'Brien speculate about the man he kills? Why do you think he does so?

6. *Why do you think O'Brien keeps referring to the man's eye, now a star-shaped hole?

7. How does the Vietnamese man's death affect O'Brien? What does Kiowa do to console him?

8. *How does the Vietnamese girl react to the death of her family? Why do you think she does this? Identify different ways in which you think people cope with death.

9. *Activity: Write a diamente poem contrasting Life and Death.

10. *Activity: Add two similes to your list. See pp. 118, 129.

Pages 137–161

1. Identify three ways in which the Vietnam War has affected Norman Bowker.

2. *What does Bowker remember about Kiowa's death? Why do you think these flashbacks keep occurring?

3. Identify the medals Bowker received for his service in Vietnam.

4. Identify the one medal Bowker did not receive and explain why this troubles him so much. Why doesn't he talk to his father about this?

5. In his letter to O'Brien, what does Bowker suggest about his writing? What effect does this have on O'Brien?

6. *What eventually happens to Bowker? What do you think causes this?

7. *Activity: Write a letter from Bowker to his father explaining his need for someone to listen to him explain why he didn't receive the Silver Star.

8. *Activity: Add one simile to your list. See p. 151.

Pages 162–188

1. Why does Jimmy Cross blame himself for Kiowa's death?

2. *When the men find Kiowa's rucksack, what is in it? What do you think this indicates about Kiowa?

3. *Explain who you think the young soldier is and why. Why does he blame himself for Kiowa's death?

4. *To what does O'Brien compare the field where Kiowa is buried, Kiowa, and the members of the platoon? What is your interpretation of these metaphors?

5. Identify two events O'Brien states are "story" truth and two events that are "happening" truth.

6. *Who returns to Vietnam with O'Brien and what is the primary thing that happens there?

7. *Why do you think O'Brien returns? Explain whether you think this is a "story" truth or a "happening" truth.

8. *Activity: Working in a small group, research Post-Traumatic Stress Disorder, then prepare a chart correlating the symptoms with those Bowker and O'Brien experience after the war.

9. *Activity: Add two similes and two metaphors to your list. See pp. 165, 167, 171.

Pages 189–218

1. How many times is O'Brien injured? Who was the medic who attended him each time?

2. *Why does O'Brien want revenge from Bobby Jorgenson? Explain why you do or do not think he is justified in feeling this way.

3. Why does O'Brien think he is transferred away from the war zone? How does he feel about this?

4. *When the men from Alpha Company return to base, how do they react to O'Brien? How does O'Brien feel about this?

5. What happens when O'Brien meets Jorgenson at base camp? What does O'Brien decide to do? Why?

6. Who is going to help O'Brien with his plans for revenge? What do they intend to do? Explain briefly what happens to O'Brien; to Azar; to Jorgenson.

7. Identify the metaphor that identifies the main "ghost" in Vietnam. How does this ghost cause problems for the Americans?

8. *How has the war changed O'Brien? Explain why you do or do not think this change is typical of other soldiers.

9. *Activity: Research near-death experiences and participate in a class discussion correlating these with O'Brien's description of his experience after he was shot near the Song Tra Bong River.

10. *Activity: Add two similes and two metaphors to your list. See pp. 200, 204, 207, 208, 209, 211, 213

Pages 219–246

1. *What does Rat Kiley do to escape active duty in Vietnam? Why does he do so? What do you think his experience signifies about men in battle?

2. *How do the Americans react to the death of the old Vietnamese man? Why do you think they do this?

3. Who is Linda? What happens to her?

4. *Why do you think O'Brien includes the story about Linda in this book?

5. What does O'Brien view as the role of stories in remembering those who have died?

6. *Explain what you think O'Brien means by his final statement, "I realize it is Tim trying to save Timmy's life with a story." Who is Tim? Who is Timmy?

7. *Activity: Write a poem or short essay in which you (a) describe what you imagine it must be like to face the death of someone close to you or (b) relate a memory of someone who has died.

8. *Activity: Add one simile and one metaphor to your list. See p. 223.

Name _____

Attribute Web

Directions: Record evidence about the narrator, Tim O'Brien (not the author).

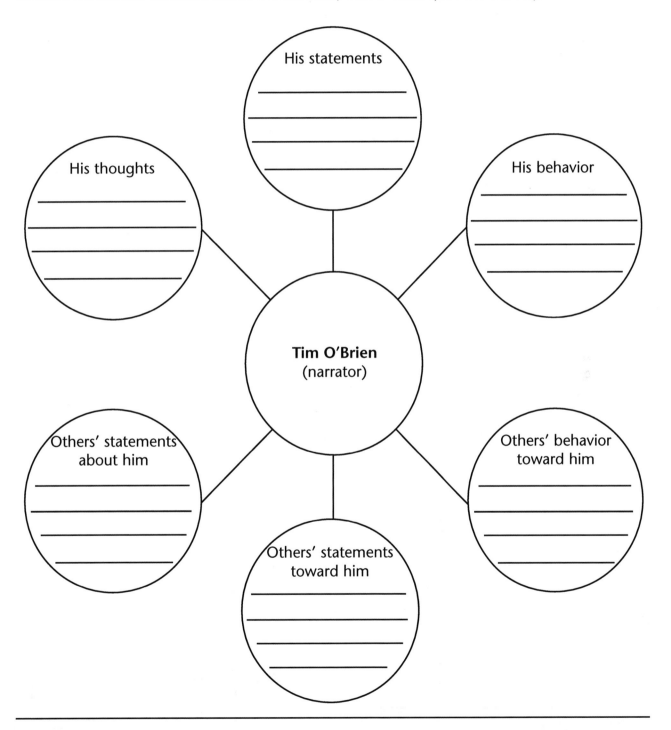

15

Sorting Characters

Directions: Similarities among characters are sometimes a clue to themes in the story. Place the book's characters in one or more of the groups below.

Victims	Victimizers	Fighters
Peace-lovers	**Conformists**	**Self-directors**

Character Reactions

Directions: On the smaller lines, describe each individual's reaction to Kiowa's death.

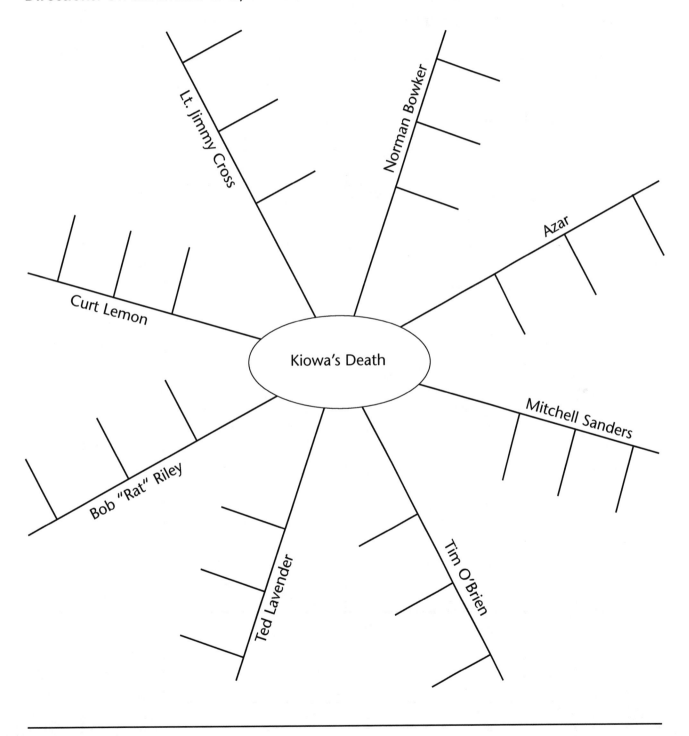

Story Map

Directions: Select five stories from the novel. In each box, place the name of the story, the primary characters, and the type of conflict in the story. Then write a one-sentence summary of the story.

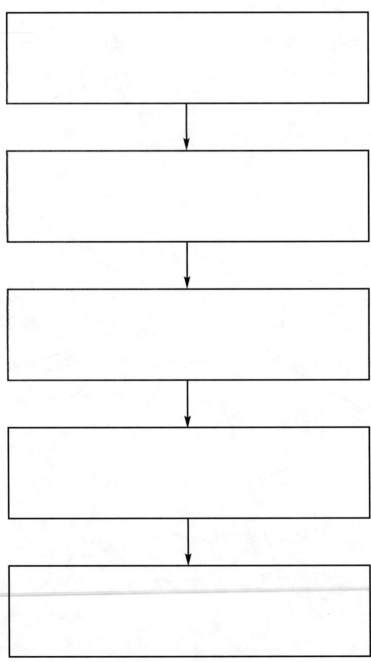

Theme Analysis

Directions: Choose a theme from the book to be the focus of your word web. Complete the web and then answer the question in each starred box.

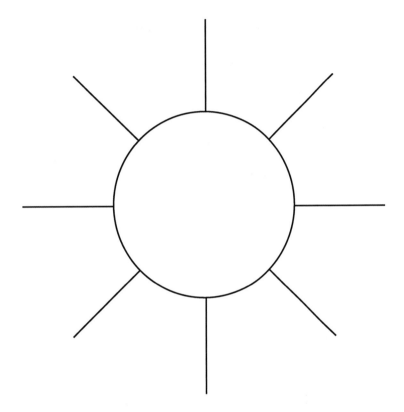

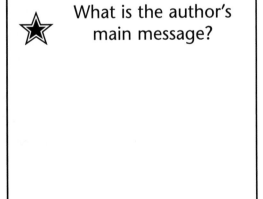

What is the author's main message?

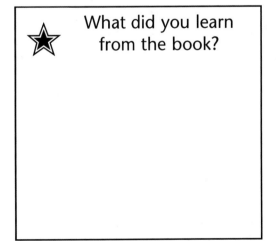

What did you learn from the book?

19

Novel Web Diagram

Directions: Place the book's title in the oval. Then fill in the boxes to summarize the novel.

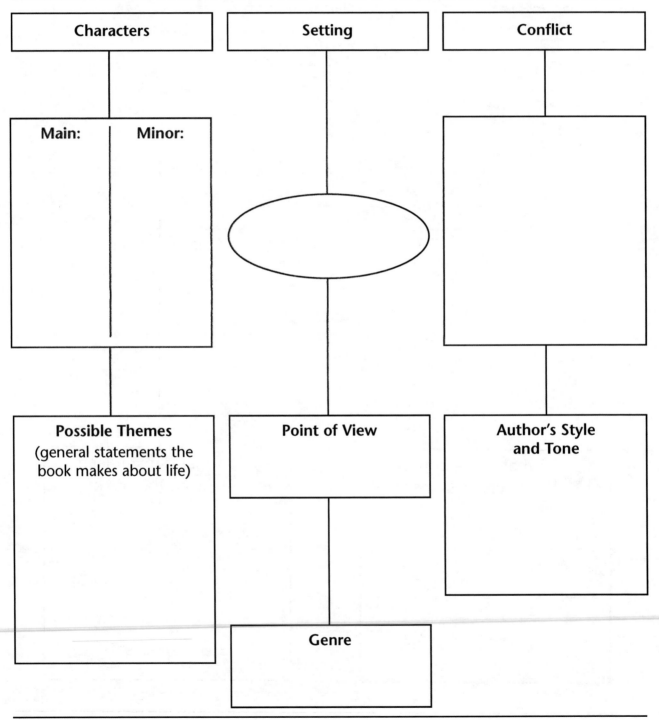

Herringbone Chart

Directions: Using one or more of the stories and your imagination, record the answers to the questions on the herringbone chart below. (Who was involved? What did these persons do? When did it happen? Where did it happen? How did it happen? Why did it happen?) Add spaces if there are more than two answers to a question. Then write a newspaper article about the incident.

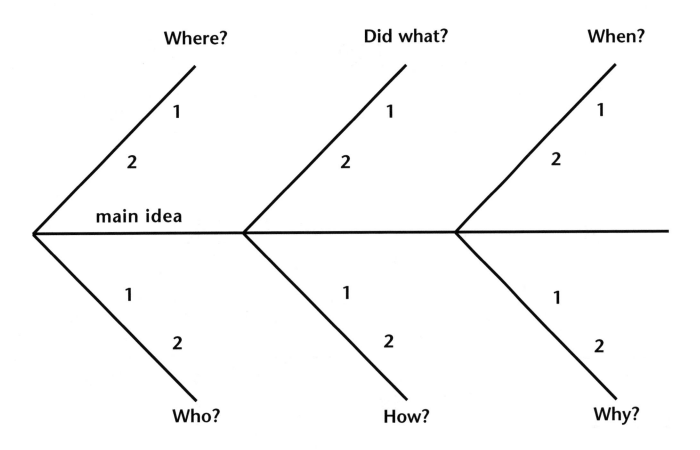

Cause/Effect Chart

Directions: Make a flow chart that shows the decision one of the characters made, the decisions the character could have made, and the results from each possible decision; for example, O'Brien's decision to get revenge on Jorgenson. Use your imagination to speculate on the results of the decision O'Brien could have made.

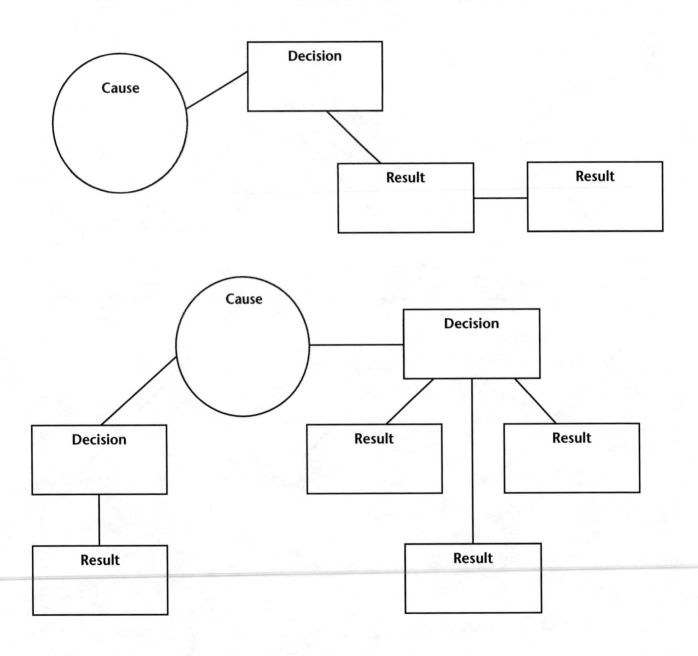

Name _____

Character Chart

Directions: Complete the following chart for the members of Alpha Company.

Name and Role in Alpha Co.	Physical/Emotional Burdens He Carries	Personal Items He Carries	What Happens to Him

Name _____

True/False

____ 1. The tangible things the men carry into Vietnam are largely determined by personal desires.

____ 2. Lt. Cross blames himself for Lavender's death.

____ 3. After Lavender's death, Kiowa's primary reaction is anger.

____ 4. According to O'Brien, men in Vietnam kill and die because of their loyalty to their country.

____ 5. Before being drafted, O'Brien takes a modest stand against the Vietnam War.

Fill in the blanks.

6. After Lavender's death, Lt. Cross burns _____.

7. O'Brien spends the summer of 1968 working _____.

8. The man who most influences O'Brien in his decision whether or not to defect to Canada is _____.

9. O'Brien says that he ultimately goes to war because _____

_____.

10. _____ visits the narrator in Massachusetts several years after the war.

11. Strunk and Jensen get into a fight over _____.

12. Strunk is mortally wounded when he _____.

Write short answers to the following questions.

1. According to O'Brien, state three ways you can identify a true war story.

2. How does Curt Lemon die?

3. Explain how the men retaliate for Lemon's death.

4. Why does Lemon have the dentist pull a healthy tooth?

5. Why does Mary Anne Bell come to Vietnam?

6. State three ways Mary Anne changes after she arrives in Vietnam

7. What eventually happens to Mary Anne?

8. What is Henry Dobbins' good-luck charm? What does he think it does for him?

9. Why is Kiowa against establishing a fortress at the pagoda?

10. How does killing a Vietnamese man affect O'Brien?

Name _____

Fill in the blanks.

1. Norman Bowker believes he failed to receive the Silver Star because _____

_____.

2. One aftereffect of the Vietnam War Bowker experiences is _____

_____.

3. Bowker writes O'Brien a letter and tells him he should write a story about _____

_____.

4. Jimmy Cross blames himself for Kiowa's death because _____

_____.

5. Lt. Cross compares the field where Kiowa is lost to a _____.

6. Give one example O'Brien uses of "happening" truth and one example of "story"

truth: _____

_____.

True/False

_____ 7. Norman Bowker received eight medals in the Vietnam War.

_____ 8. Bowker wishes he could talk to Lt. Cross about Kiowa's death.

_____ 9. Bowker commits suicide.

_____ 10. O'Brien returns to Vietnam with his wife and daughter.

_____ 11. O'Brien places Kiowa's moccasins in the muck at the edge of the field where
        he died.

True/False

_____ 1. O'Brien is injured three times in Vietnam.

_____ 2. When O'Brien is reunited with the men of Alpha Company at base camp, he no longer feels the same camaraderie with them.

_____ 3. Sanders agrees to help O'Brien in his plan for revenge on Jorgenson.

_____ 4. The Vietnam War has made O'Brien hard and cruel.

_____ 5. Rat Kiley shoots himself in the foot.

_____ 6. O'Brien thinks it is offensive to tell stories about dead people.

Write short answers to the following questions.

7. Why does O'Brien want revenge on Jorgenson?

8. Why does O'Brien think he is transferred away from the war zone?

9. What is the end result of O'Brien's revenge?

10. What is the main "ghost" in Vietnam and how does this ghost cause problems for the Americans?

11. Who is Linda and what happens to her?

Name _____

A. Identification: Match each character with the correct description, using each name only once. (2 pts. each)

____ 1.	Tim O'Brien	a.	cruel and unkind; makes crude jokes about death
____ 2.	Jimmy Cross	b.	kind; wants everyone to be treated fairly
____ 3.	Mary Anne Bell	c.	narrator; conveys horrors of Vietnam War
____ 4.	Mitchell Sanders	d.	medic; brave and efficient
____ 5.	Norman Bowker	e.	religious; dies in a slimy field
____ 6.	Rat Kiley	f.	platoon leader; feels responsible for all his men
____ 7.	Kiowa	g.	saves a young man from defecting to Canada
____ 8.	Azar	h.	innocent, attractive; fascinated with war; disappears
____ 9.	Curt Lemon	i.	quiet, introspective; eventually commits suicide
____ 10.	Elroy Berdahl	j.	brags and exaggerates; dies a horrible death

B. Multiple Choice: Choose the BEST answer. (2 pts. each)

____ 11. The things the men carry into Vietnam are largely determined by
(a) personal desire
(b) choice
(c) necessity
(d) chance

____ 12. Lt. Cross blames himself for Lavender's death because he
(a) thinks he loves Martha more than his men
(b) knows he should have shot the sniper
(c) led his men down the wrong path
(d) didn't order him to retreat

___13. O'Brien believes he doesn't defect to Canada because
    (a) of his loyalty to his country
    (b) he loves the feel of victory
    (c) it is necessary to stamp out Communism
    (d) he is embarrassed not to

___14. O'Brien's view of war is
    (a) you just follow orders
    (b) you don't make war without knowing why
    (c) you have to trust the rulers of the country
    (d) war is never justified

___15. Elroy Berdahl influences O'Brien
    (a) to volunteer for the Army
    (b) to become a reservist
    (c) not to go to Canada
    (d) not to go to war

___16. The narrator says he decides to go to war because he
    (a) is a loyal citizen
    (b) believes it is for a just cause
    (c) is a coward
    (d) wants to receive veteran's benefits

___17. O'Brien continues to be haunted for twenty years by
    (a) memories of Curt Lemon's death
    (b) memories of his defection
    (c) questions of whether he should have gone to war
    (d) memories of Cross's death

___18. The death of the water buffalo symbolizes
    (a) justice
    (b) mindless retaliation
    (c) desperation for food
    (d) the sport of hunting

___19. O'Brien says war is all but which one of the following?
    (a) hell
    (b) courage
    (c) love
    (d) fulfilling

___20. The story of Mary Anne Bell symbolizes
    (a) the death of innocence
    (b) women in war
    (c) unfair treatment of women
    (d) the whimsical nature of a woman

___21. Kiowa believes that setting up a fortress at the pagoda is
    (a) safe
    (b) sacrilegious
    (c) unsafe
    (d) foolish

___22. O'Brien speculates that the man he kills
    (a) had always wanted to be a hero
    (b) planned to immigrate to the United States
    (c) had never wanted to be a soldier
    (d) was a factory laborer

___23. Kathleen thinks her dad keeps writing war stories because he
    (a) must have killed someone
    (b) needs the money
    (c) doesn't like an office job
    (d) wants to portray the glories of war

___24. Norman Bowker is haunted by
    (a) his inability to become a lieutenant
    (b) memories of his serious wounds
    (c) his father's abuse
    (d) Kiowa's death

___25. Bowker's response to the war includes all but which one of the following?
(a) self-pity
(b) guilt
(c) overt belligerence
(d) feigned indifference

___26. Jimmy Cross blames himself for Kiowa's death because he
(a) sent him to the front lines
(b) should have moved the platoon to higher ground
(c) failed to throw the grenade in time
(d) lost contact with base headquarters

___27. Azar copes with death in Vietnam by
(a) daydreaming about his girlfriend
(b) writing stories
(c) making crude jokes
(d) talking to a psychiatrist

___28. In his mental letter to Kiowa's father, Lt. Cross first plans to
(a) blame the United States for entering the war
(b) apologize and admit his own blunders
(c) ask him if he wants Kiowa's belongings
(d) tell him he doesn't know what happened to Kiowa

___29. The young soldier, O'Brien, blames himself for Kiowa's death because
(a) his flashlight revealed their position
(b) he asked Kiowa to take his place
(c) Kiowa threw himself on the grenade for him
(d) he didn't warn Kiowa about the sniper

___30. After the men find Kiowa's body, they
(a) dig a grave and bury him
(b) are consumed with fear for their lives
(c) wish they had never found him
(d) feel a secret joy because they are alive

___31. O'Brien recants his story about killing a man but blames himself for the death
because
(a) he gave the orders to fire
(b) he didn't warn him
(c) he was there
(d) he could have saved him but didn't

___32. According to O'Brien, a "happening" truth is
(a) he killed a man
(b) there were many bodies but he was afraid to look
(c) he never went to Vietnam
(d) he never had a chance to see a dead Vietnamese

___33. O'Brien returns to Vietnam with his daughter
(a) in search of forgiveness and grace
(b) because he has just gotten a divorce
(c) in search of Kiowa
(d) to receive the Silver Star

___34. O'Brien finds closure for his Vietnam experience by
(a) writing the story of Lavender's death
(b) placing Kiowa's moccasins in the field where he died
(c) writing the story about Bowker
(d) reminiscing about the war with Lt. Cross

___35. O'Brien plans to avenge his maltreatment by Jorgenson by
(a) shooting his foot
(b) reporting Jorgenson to the commander
(c) forcing Jorgenson to look at his injuries
(d) messing with Jorgenson's head

___36. O'Brien identifies the main "ghost" of Vietnam as
(a) himself
(b) Azar
(c) Charlie Cong
(d) the memories

Name _____

___37. The psychological effects of war on Rat Kiley come to a climax when
(a) O'Brien is injured
(b) the platoon returns to base camp
(c) some of the men play cruel jokes on him
(d) the platoon must live the night life

___38. O'Brien's first experience with death in Vietnam triggers his memory of
(a) Linda's death
(b) his mother's death
(c) his father's death
(d) Elroy Berdahl

___39. O'Brien believes he can keep the dead alive
(a) by buying a memorial for them
(b) with stories
(c) with pictures of them
(d) by visiting their graves

___40. "Her eyes were as fluffy and airy-light as cotton candy" is an example of
(a) metaphor
(b) irony
(c) personification
(d) simile

___41. "Imagination was a killer" is an example of
(a) metaphor
(b) simile
(c) stream-of-consciousness
(d) alliteration

C. Essay: Choose one of the following and respond in a well-developed paragraph of at least five sentences. (10 pts.)

    (a) Choose one of the novel's themes and explain how it is developed. Cite examples from the book to support your answer.

    (b) Explain why you do or do not think the title is appropriate.

    (c) Explain some of the emotional burdens the men of Alpha Company acquire in Vietnam.

D. Creative Response: Choose one of the following. (10 pts.)

    (a) Write name poems for three of the characters.

    (b) Write a letter from Jimmy Cross to Kiowa's father explaining Kiowa's death.

    (c) Write a five-senses poem about anxiety, loneliness, or guilt.

A. Identification: Write two to four words that characterize each of the following. (1 pt. each)

Character	Primary Characteristics	Significance to the novel
1. Jimmy Cross		
2. Tim O'Brien		
3. Kiowa		
4. Mitchell Sanders		
5. Azar		
6. Elroy Berdahl		
7. Mary Anne Bell		
8. Norman Bowker		
9. Rat Kiley		
10. Curt Lemon		

B. Multiple Choice: Choose the BEST answer. (2 pts. each)

___11. Individual men of Alpha Company carry all but which one of the following into Vietnam?
(a) girl's pantyhose
(b) tranquilizers
(c) propaganda literature
(d) New Testament

___12. According to O'Brien, the men in Vietnam kill and die because
(a) they will be court martialed if they don't
(b) they are embarrassed not to
(c) of their loyalty to their country
(d) they love fighting

___13. O'Brien says he submits to the draft because
(a) he is a coward
(b) he is a hero
(c) his father tells him that's the right thing to do
(d) he knows he'll go to prison if he doesn't

___14. The field where Kiowa dies symbolizes
 (a) the end result of debauchery
 (b) the sadness of death
 (c) eternal life
 (d) all the waste that was Vietnam

___15. All but which one of the following blames himself for Kiowa's death?
 (a) Bowker
 (b) Kiley
 (c) O'Brien
 (d) Cross

___16. O'Brien's thoughts as he contemplates defecting to Canada include all but which one of the following?
 (a) realizes Canada is a pitiful fantasy
 (b) realizes he will not do what he should do
 (c) feels it is the right moral choice to submit to the draft
 (d) feels he should go to Canada

___17. A true war story does all but which one of the following?
 (a) never moralizes
 (b) will embarrass the listener
 (c) never seems to end
 (d) instructs the listener

___18. O'Brien speculates that the man he killed was, above anything else,
 (a) afraid of disgracing himself
 (b) determined to kill an American
 (c) anxious to return to his home
 (d) dissatisfied with the Communist regime

___19. Bowker's letter to O'Brien sums up the reaction of many returning vets in their
 (a) hatred for the Vietnamese people
 (b) problems of finding a meaningful use for their lives
 (c) problems in their marriages
 (d) aversion for the military

___20. The tone of the book is best described as
   (a) insincere
   (b) unclear
   (c) forthright
   (d) vindictive

C. Short Answer: On a separate sheet of paper, write brief answers to the following questions. (2 pts. each)

21. Why does Lt. Cross blame himself for Lavender's death?

22. What does the killing of the baby water buffalo symbolize?

23. What does the story of Mary Anne Bell symbolize?

24. Why does Kathleen think her dad keeps writing war stories?

25. Why does Kiowa's death continue to haunt Norman Bowker after he returns to the United States?

26. How does Azar most often cope with death in Vietnam?

27. What action of O'Brien's symbolizes closure for his Vietnam experience?

28. How does O'Brien plan to revenge himself against Jorgenson?

29. What does O'Brien identify as the main ghost in Vietnam?

30. What is the end result of the psychological effects of the war on Rat Kiley?

31. What memory does O'Brien's first experience with death in Vietnam trigger?

32. How does O'Brien believe he can keep the dead alive?

33. What memory of Kiowa haunts O'Brien? Why?

34. Why does Bowker think he failed to receive the Silver Star for valor?

35. Identify three men of Alpha Company who survive the war and three who die in Vietnam.

D. Identification: Identify the following literary devices. (2 pts. each)

36. _____: They moved like moles.
37. _____: War is hell.
38. _____: I was Nam.
39. _____: I felt as if I were hurtling down a huge black funnel.

E. Essay: Choose one of the following and answer in a well-developed paragraph of at least seven sentences. (10 pts.)

   (a) Explain how the novel emphasizes the human side of the soldiers rather than their strength and courageous accomplishments.

   (b) Explain O'Brien's development of the statement, "When a man died, there had to be blame." Give specific examples from the novel.

   (c) Explain what you think O'Brien means by the final statement in the novel, "...when I take a high leap into the dark and come down thirty years later, I realize it is as Tim trying to save Timmy's life with a story." Give examples from the novel.

F. Creative Response: Choose one of the following (10 pts.)

   (a) Write a newspaper article about the reunion of Alpha Company in the year 2000.

   (b) Choose one of the stories and retell it in a letter.

   (c) Write a poetic lament about Kiowa's death.

Answer Key

Activities #1 & #2: Responses will vary.

Activity #3: 1. s 2. j 3. f 4. t 5. a 6. o 7. r 8. e 9. b 10. p 11. d 12. g 13. m 14. h 15. i 16. n 17. l 18. q 19. c 20. k

Activity #4: 1. aesthetic 2. endorphins 3. rectitude 4. sadism 5. Cadres 6. mundane 7. hamlet 8. anarchy 9. surreal 10. superlatives 11. pagoda 12. Napalm 13. piasters 14. opaque 15. eccentricity 16. ordnance 17. trite 18. imprecision 19. talisman 20. digressions

Activity #5: 1. Valor 2. Latrine 3. Condolences 4. Virtues 5. Anthology 6. Irony 7. Complicity 8. Affluent 9. Tactically 10. Elusive 11. Metaphoric 12. Catharsis

Activity #6: Charts will vary. Example—Word: inert; Synonyms: lazy, dormant, inactive, motionless; Antonyms: active, working, industrious, lively; Definition in own words: being unable to move or act; Word in sentence: The heart attack victim lies inert on the stretcher.

Study Guide, pp. 1–26: 1. Cross: platoon leader of Alpha Company; equipment: compass, maps, code books, binoculars, pistol, strobe light; personal items: picture of and letters from Martha; emotional burden: responsibility for lives of his men; blame and guilt when they die (pp. 3–5, 11–16, 16–17, 23–24) 2. the girl he loves but who doesn't love him romantically; Answers will vary. Idea: symbolizes his method of escaping the horrors of war and his hopes for a future (pp. 4–5, 8–9) 3. because Cross was thinking about Martha and thinks Lavender died because he loved Martha more than his men; Answers will vary (pp. 16–17). 4. men and tangible items—Mitchell sanders, RTO: radio, condoms; Rat Kiley, medic: medical bag, comic books, brandy. Henry Dobbins, machine gunner: M-60 and ammunition, his girlfriend's pantyhose; Ted Lavender: tranquilizers; Norman Bowker: diary, thumb from a VC corpse; Dave Jensen: night-sight vitamins, rabbit's foot; Lee Strunk: slingshot. All men carry some kind of equipment and survival necessities; most carry photographs; sometimes they carry each other. Intangibles: ghosts such as memories, love, and fear; cowardice. They fight because of their fear of revealing their cowardice (pp. 2–22). 5. Cross: blames himself, cries for a long time; Kiowa: feels guilty because he is glad to be alive; Bowker: angry at Kiowa because he won't talk about it. Some tell stories and make jokes about Lavender's drug use; Responses will vary (pp. 16–21). 6. Freedom birds are jumbo jets that will carry them far away from the war (pp. 22–23). 7. Responses will vary. 8. Activity 9. Activity

Pages 27–38: 1. Responses will vary but should include the more personal response to memories (pp. 27–28). 2. Jimmy Cross; memories of the war and their buddies are vivid for both of them; Cross still blames himself for Lavender's death (pp. 27–30). 3. as the best platoon leader ever; he is trying to overcome the guilt and blame he feels for the deaths of some of his men (pp. 27–30). 4. terror and violence: Kiowa sinking into the deep muck of the latrine; Lemon hanging in pieces from a tree; death of the young Vietnamese soldier; Responses will vary (pp. 32, 37). 5. sweetness and gentleness: Azar giving candy to a maimed Vietnamese child; an old man guiding the platoon through the minefields; Kiowa teaching a rain dance to Kiley and Jensen; Lavender adopting an orphan puppy; Responses will vary (pp. 33–36). 6. Activity 7. Activity

Pages 39–66: 1. He thought the story would cause embarrassment; hopes to relieve the pressure of his dreams (p. 39). 2. startled; silently screaming; thinks he is too good, compassionate, and smart for this war; discovers that he is a coward instead of the hero he thought he would be (pp. 39–41) 3. before—mild protests such as ringing doorbells for McCarthy and writing editorials for campus newspaper; feels no personal danger until draft notice arrives; after—hates the idea of war; totally against it; thinks he can never become a soldier because he hates dirt, tents, mosquitoes, blood, and authority; feels emotions ranging from self-pity to numbness (pp. 40–42). 4. removes blood clots from necks of pigs who have been slaughtered in a meatpacking plant; correlates with future experiences in Vietnam (pp. 42–43) 5. graduate school deferments, National Guard, Reserves, medical condition, Conscientious Objector, defecting to another country; defection; very few

---

deferments being given, long waiting lists for Guards and Reserves, is in good health (pp. 43–44) 6. escape to Canada; fears war but also fears losing respect of his parents and being pursued by the law; experiences emotions of outrage, terror, bewilderment, guilt, and sorrow. Physically: vomiting, sweating, dizzy, can't sleep or lie still. Mentally: thinks he's gone off the psychic edge; can't tell up from down; sees weird pictures in his mind (pp. 44–48). 7. owner of Tip Top Lodge, close to the Canadian border, where O'Brien stays six days; helps him open up and talk about his life; brings him to the point of choosing between going to war and fleeing to Canada (pp. 48–56) 8. decides not to flee but to return and submit to the draft; believes he should flee from the war but doesn't do so because he can't risk the embarrassment; goes to war because he is a coward; Responses will vary (pp. 56–61). 9. over a missing jackknife; Jensen breaks Stunk's nose, then is afraid Strunk will kill him; starts firing randomly; breaks own nose to square things with Strunk. The tenseness of war makes men fight over frivolous things (pp. 62–66). 10. Activity 11. Activity

Pages 67–88: 1. true war story: never moral, doesn't instruct or teach a virtue, contains obscenity and evil, will embarrass the listener, alludes to war being "fun," never seems to end, cannot be believed, does not generalize, makes the stomach believe (pp. 66–85) 2. Responses will vary. Suggestions: Kiley's story doesn't teach a moral, includes obscenity and evil, tries to make war fun, doesn't make the reader feel uplifted. Sanders' story has a moral, i.e., nobody listens, he admits part of it is fabricated (pp. 67–68, 72–76). 3. steps on a booby trap that blows him up, with body pieces hanging in the trees; The sickening sight and necessity of retrieving the pieces makes O'Brien sick (pp. 82–84). 4. The other men find and rope the animal. Rat Kiley begins to shoot it repeatedly and mercilessly, then the others dump its body in a well. The men react because of their rage and grief over Lemon's death (pp. 78–80, 85). 5. Responses will vary. Ideas: Evil invades Vietnam because of the war just as original sin invaded the Garden of Eden in the Bible; after the war, Vietnam will never be the same just as the Garden of Eden was never the same (pp. 80–81). 6. War is hell but also mystery, courage, love, etc.; almost everything is true yet almost nothing is true; makes you a man but makes you dead; nasty/fun, ugly/beautiful, right/wrong, law/anarchy (pp. 80–82). 7. so afraid he passes out; to prove his courage (pp. 86–88) 8. Activity 9. Activity

Pages 89–116: 1. Mary Anne Bell is Mark Fossie's girlfriend; he is a soldier and she comes to Vietnam to be with him; Responses will vary (pp. 93–94). 2. no longer cares about her physical appearance; is not intimidated by blood or fear; learns how to assemble and use weapons; becomes vague about future plans with Mark; participates in rituals associated with the hunt and kill of war (pp. 89–112) 3. She is going on ambushes with the Green Berets (pp. 101–102). 4. She joins with the Green Berets and later disappears into the mountains in Vietnam and is never seen again (pp. 112–116). 5. Responses will vary. Suggestion: changes symbolize the effect on Vietnam on those who fight; death of innocence (p. 114). 6. The military forces are one big zoo, with the "animals" expected to conform and perform while their "keepers," commanders and political forces, command them. The soldiers lose their individuality in their struggle to survive. They become more like animals than humans (p. 107). 7. Activity 8. Activity

Pages 117–136: 1. Responses will vary. Idea: for a variation in tone; less horrific 2. his girlfriend's pantyhose; like body armor that will keep him safe (pp. 117–118) 3. thinks it is bad news and is wrong because the pagoda is a church (pp. 119–122) 4. Responses will vary. Idea: try to wash their hands of the evil, death, and destruction of the war (pp. 119–123) 5. that he might have been a scholar who fights because he loves Vietnam, not because he's a Communist; believes he hates violence but goes to war to keep from disgracing himself; thinks he has fallen in love even though he knows he will die in the war; Answers will vary. Ideas: to give a face to the enemy, to help the readers "believe in the stomach" (pp. 124–128) 6. Responses will vary. Ideas: that is the most startling of his injuries; since the star-shaped hole replaces the eye, the light of life has gone out (pp. 124–128). 7. He feels guilty because he thinks the man would have passed by without seeing the Americans; he stares at the body and won't leave the death scene (pp. 126–134). 8. dancing, smiling to herself dreamily, putting her hands over her ears; this is her defense mechanism to escape the reality of the deaths of her family members; Answers will vary (pp. 135–136). 9. Activity 10. Activity

Pages 137–161: 1. constantly in motion; has nowhere to go; dwells on things that happened before Vietnam; has flashbacks about Kiowa's death; remembers his failure to receive the Silver Star (pp. 137–155) 2. remembers Kiowa sinking into the slimy water of the latrine field, the terrible smell, and letting go of Kiowa's boot as he slipped into the filthy water; blames himself for Kiowa's death (pp. 141–149) 3. Combat Infantryman's Badge, Air Medal, Army Commendation Medal, Good Conduct Medal, Vietnam Campaign Medal, Bronze Star, Purple Heart (p. 141) 4. Silver Star, given for uncommon valor; thinks he would have received this medal if he had saved Kiowa's life; thinks most people in the town, including his father, would not like to hear the horrors of the war (pp. 141–142) 5. He should write a story about a guy who can never get his act together because he is haunted by Kiowa's death and wants to talk about it but can't; disrupts O'Brien's feeling of smugness about his easy adjustment to life after the war. O'Brien includes a chapter about Bowker in the book he is writing (pp. 157–159). 6. He commits suicide by hanging himself; he never adjusted to life after Vietnam and could never forget the horror of the war (p. 155). 7. Activity 8. Activity

Pages 162–188: 1. thinks he should not have had the platoon set up camp on the edge of the river or should have moved the camp to higher ground (p. 164) 2. a pair of moccasins and a New Testament; Answers will vary (p. 166). 3. The young man is O'Brien; Answers will vary; feels guilty for Kiowa's death because he was using a flashlight to show Kiowa a picture of his girlfriend, and the flashlight made a perfect target for enemy fire (p. 170). 4. Field: a golf course; Kiowa: lost ball; members of the platoon: those who play the game; Interpretations will vary (p. 167). 5. Story—truth: the narrator killed a young Vietnamese man; happening—truth: there were many bodies in Vietnam, but the narrator was afraid to look at them; feels responsibility and grief (p. 180). 6. his daughter Kathleen; O'Brien returns to the field where Kiowa died, goes into the slimy water, and submerges Kiowa's moccasins (pp. 181, 184–188). 7. Responses will vary; Ideas: O'Brien needs to find closure for his years in Vietnam, especially Kiowa's death (inference); Responses will vary. 8. Activity 9. Activity

Pages 189–218: 1. two; Rat Kiley the first time; Bobby Jorgenson the second (pp. 189–190) 2. O'Brien almost dies because of Jorgensen's slow response and his inept attention to O'Brien's wounds, which result in a massive infection; Responses will vary (pp. 190–191). 3. He believes the higher-ups think he has been shot enough; mixed feelings—glad to be reasonably safe but sometimes misses the adventure and camaraderie of the battlefield (pp. 191–192). 4. They share stories of which O'Brian is not a part, tease him about his injury, and let him know that Jorgenson is now "one of them." O'Brien feels left out and betrayed, as if he has forfeited membership in the group (pp. 193– 198). 5. They speak; Jorgenson apologizes and offers to shake hands, but O'Brien refuses and decides to get revenge by "messing with his mind" (pp. 198–201). 6. Azar—rigs flares, ropes, rattle, tear-gas grenades, and a sandbag with which to spook Jorgenson while he is on guard duty and make him think the enemy is all around him; O'Brien—wants to back out but Azar won't let him; finally tells Azar to quit; Azar kicks him in the head; Azar—thoroughly enjoys the tormenting "game"; after kicking O'Brien, he goes off to bed; Jorgenson—becomes spooked but does not panic; fires at the sandbag; realizes it's O'Brien and calls out his name; treats O'Brien's head wound. O'Brien and Jorgenson agree they're even and shake hands (pp. 206–218). 7. "It was ghost country, and Charlie Cong was the main ghost." They feel as if the land is haunted and they are fighting an unseen, evil force that appears and disappears. The "ghost" comes out silently at night, the men never really see him but think they do; they think he can levitate, fly, pass through barbed wire, and melt away like ice (p. 202). 8. His civilized, hopeful view of life is crushed; he has turned mean inside and can be cruel; he feels cold inside, realizes he is capable of evil, and has become vindictive against anyone who harms him (p. 200). 9. Activity 10. Activity

Pages 219–246: 1. shoots himself in the foot; psychological reaction to the war, especially two weeks of moving at night and trying to sleep in the daytime, seeing too many body bags and too much gore, cause him to break under the strain; Responses will vary (pp. 219–224). 2. prop the body against a fence, call him the guest of honor, propose toasts to him, and shake hands with him; Responses will vary; Ideas: make death less horrific (pp. 225–226) 3. O'Brien's childhood girlfriend; she dies when she is nine years old from a brain tumor (pp. 228–236). 4. Responses will vary. Ideas: The old man is the first death O'Brien experiences in Vietnam; Linda was his first experience with death. His memories of the old man, of Lavender, and Linda mingle together (pp. 224–231). 5. Stories keep the dead alive (pp. 238–239). 6. Responses will vary. Ideas: As O'Brien writes the stories of Vietnam, he depicts the horrors of war and allows himself to deal with personal memories of the trauma and violence. Tim O'Brien, the author, tries to save his own life by encountering his memories of war to set himself free to live. "Timmy" is the innocence of "Tim," before he encountered the death of his friend at nine years old, also the "Timmy" before he went to war. 7. Activity 8. Activity

Note: Responses to Activities #7–#15 will vary. This guide offers suggested answers.

Activity #7: Statements: Speaking of the story about Lemon's death and the death of the water buffalo, "It wasn't a war story. It was a love story. None of it happened. Even if it had did happen, it didn't happen on the mountains, it happened in this little village on the Batangan Peninsula." To Kathleen after placing Kiowa's moccasins in the field, "All that's finished." Behavior: attempts to defect to Canada; sickened by death in Vietnam; struggles to find closure. Fears: being thought a coward; death. Thoughts: War is hell; but he also thinks it is mystery, terror, adventure, discovery, holiness, and a myriad of other emotions. Memories of smells, especially the field of human waste and mud, and the men who died and those who lived; plots revenge against Jorgenson. Looks: young, innocent. Others' actions toward him: respectful, supportive, occasionally mocking.

Activity #8: Victims—men of Alpha Company, Viet Cong, citizens of Vietnam, Mary Anne, baby hippo; Victimizers—men of Alpha Company, Viet Cong, Marry Anne; Fighters—men of Alpha company, Viet Cong, Mary Anne; Peace-lovers—Tim O'Brien, Kiowa, Elroy Berdahl, Norman Bowker, Mitchell Sanders, all the men of Alpha Company; Comformists—Tim O'Brien, all men of Alpha Company, Viet Cong; Self-directors—Rat Kiley, Elroy Berdahl, Mary Anne

Activity #9: Lt. Jimmy Cross: blames himself because he ordered the platoon to camp next to the river; Norman Bowker: blames himself for letting go of Kiowa's boot and letting him slip into the muddy sewage; Azar: makes crude jokes at first but feels ill and apologizes for jokes when they find his body; Mitchell Sanders: blames Cross for having them camp next to a field of human waste and mud; Tim O'Brien: blames himself for using a flashlight that illuminated their position

Activity #10: (1) "On the Rainy River": Tim O'Brien, Elroy Berdahl; O'Brien's inner conflict. Elroy Berdahl helps O'Brien as he struggles with whether to submit to the draft or escape to Canada; O'Brien stays in the United States. (2) "Sweetheart of the Song Tra Bong": Mary Anne Bell, Mark Fossie; conflict between Mary Anne and Mark; Mary Anne's inner conflict. Mary Anne comes to Vietnam to be with Fossie, becomes intrigued with and part of the war, and finally disappears into the mountains of Vietnam. (3) "The Man I Killed": O'Brien, dead young Vietnamese man, Kiowa; O'Brien's inner conflict over killing the man. O'Brien feels guilty for killing a Vietnamese man, and Kiowa consoles him and advises him to let it go. (4) "Speaking of Courage": Norman Bowker; inner conflict over Kiowa's death and failing to receive the Silver Star. Norman Bowker reflects on the war, blames himself for Kiowa's death, and believes he would have received the Silver Star for saving Kiowa. (5) "In the Field": Kiowa, O'Brien, Cross, Bowker; war conflict; inner conflict of the three men who blame themselves for Kiowa's death. Kiowa is killed by sniper fire, and the men of the platoon search for his body, each relives his guilt for the death.

Activity #11: Theme: Isolation; Spokes: O'Brien's silent mental anguish after receiving the draft notice; Bowker's feeling that no one cares about what happened to him in Vietnam; O'Brien's loss of camaraderie with the other men; Cross's mental suffering after the deaths of his men; all the men in the hostile enemy territory; Bowker's ultimate suicide; Mary Anne's retreat from things she has known and loved; O'Brien's mental anguish after killing a man; Kiley's retreat into psychological stress. Main message: War causes men to carry mental, physical and emotional items.

Activity #12: Characters: Main—Tim O'Brien [narrator], Jimmy Cross, Ted Lavender, Mitchell Sanders, Norman Bowker, "Rat" Kiley, Kiowa, Azar, Curt Lemon; Minor—Henry Dobbins, Dave Jensen, Lee Strunk, Elroy Berdahl, Mary Anne Bell, Mark Fossie, Kathleen. Themes: psychological stress, anxiety, shame/embarrassment, fear, loneliness, survival, guilt, blame, isolation, violence, truth, memory. Setting: Vietnam, United States. Point of View: primarily first-person with some stories in third person omniscient. Genre: fiction with some factual details. Conflict: United States vs. Viet Cong; person vs. self, person vs. person, person vs. government. Author's Style and Tone: narrative; candid.

Activity #13: Story: "In the Field." Who: Kiowa, O'Brien, Cross, Bowker, other members of the platoon; What: Kiowa dies; others blame themselves for his death; they search for his body; Where: former latrine near edge of river; How: sniper fire hits Kiowa; Why: war; a flashlight illuminated their position.

Activity #14: Cause: Jorgenson's slow response and inept treatment almost kill O'Brien; Decision: O'Brien will seek revenge; Result: Azar helps him rig up equipment to mimic the enemy; Result: Jorgenson becomes alarmed but does not panic; he and O'Brien agree that they're equal. Cause: O'Brien nearly dies because of Jorgenson; Possible Decision (1): O'Brien reports him to his superiors; Result: Jorgenson is disciplined. Possible Decision (2): O'Brien chooses to forget it; Result: the other men respect him; Result: O'Brien doesn't get involved with Azar's cruelty; Result: He and Jorgenson become friends.

Activity #15: Sample answer: Lt. Jimmy Cross, platoon leader—responsibility for the lives of his men, letters from and pictures of Martha; compass, maps, code books, binoculars, pistol, strobe light, good-luck pebble; survives

Quiz 1: 1. F (p. 2) 2. T (p. 6) 3. F (p. 18) 4. F (p. 21) 5. T (pp. 41–42) 6. Martha's letters and pictures (p. 23) 7. in a meatpacking plant (p. 42) 8. Elroy Berdahl (p. 48) 9. he is a coward or he doesn't want to be embarrassed (pp. 59, 61) 10. Jimmy Cross (p. 27) 11. a missing jackknife (p. 62) 12. steps on a rigged mortar round (pp. 65–68)

Quiz 2: 1. it's never moral, will contain obscenity and evil, cannot be believed, makes the stomach believe (pp. 67–76) 2. steps on a booby trap (pp. 69–70) 3. torture and kill a water buffalo (pp. 78–80) 4. to prove his courage after passing out when he first went to the dentist (pp. 86–88) 5. to be with Mark Fossie, her boyfriend (pp. 93–94) 6. quits caring about her physical appearance, learns to assemble and use weapons, disappears for hours, participates in rituals about the hunt and kill of war (pp. 95–107) 7. disappears into mountains of Vietnam (pp. 115–116) 8. his girlfriend's pantyhose; becomes his body armor and protects him (p. 117) 9. thinks it's bad news and wrong (pp. 119–122) 10. He sits and stares, can't talk about it, always remembers and lives with regret (pp. 124–130).

Quiz 3: 1. he didn't save Kiowa's life (pp. 140–150) 2. his constant need to be moving; his inability to keep a job; flashbacks (pp. 137–138, 155–156) 3. Bowker: a guy who feels like he got zapped in the field of human waste and mud in Vietnam (p. 157) 4. he feels he should have had platoon establish camp on higher ground (pp. 162–164) 5. golf course (p. 167) 6. Happening: he was a soldier, saw many bodies but was afraid to look, feels responsible for a death; Story: he killed a young man (p. 180). 7. F (p. 140) 8. F (pp. 141–142) 9. T (p. 155) 10. F (p. 181) 11. T (pp. 186–187)

Quiz 4: 1. F (p. 189) 2. T (pp. 194–195) 3. F (pp. 197–198) 4. T (p. 200) 5. T (p. 223) 6. F (p. 239) 7. His slow, inept treatment almost killed him (pp. 184–190). 8. has been shot two times (p. 193) 9. He and Jorgenson shake hands and agree they're even (pp. 217–218). 10. Charlie Cong, the enemy; Answers will vary; Ideas: he seems to be everywhere and is invincible (p. 202). 11. O'Brien's childhood girlfriend; dies from a brain tumor when she is nine years old (pp. 228–236)

Final Test, Level One: (A) 1. c 2. f 3. h 4. b 5. i 6. d 7. e 8. a 9. j 10. g **(B)** 11. c (p. 2) 12. a (p. 6) 13. d (p. 21) 14. b (p. 41) 15. c (p. 48) 16. c (p. 61) 17. a (pp. 71, 83) 18. b (pp. 78–79) 19. d (p. 80) 20. a (pp. 105, 114) 21. b (p. 119) 22. c (p. 127) 23. a (p. 131) 24. d (pp. 148–149) 25. c (p. 156) 26. b (p. 160) 27. c (p. 165) 28. b (p. 169) 29. a (pp. 170–171) 30. d (p. 175) 31. c (p. 179) 32. b (p. 180) 33. a (p. 181) 34. b (pp. 186–188) 35. d (p. 201) 36. c (p. 202) 37. d (pp. 219–223) 38. a (pp. 227–228) 39. b (p. 239) 40. d (p. 151) 41. a (p. 80) **(C&D)** Responses will vary.

Final Test, Level Two: (A) 1. conscientious, reflective, courageous; leader of the platoon 2. introspective, sensitive, caring; author, narrator 3. religious, caring, brave; dies in slimy river, others blame themselves for his death 4. kind, impartial, devoted to others; member of platoon, wants everyone to be treated fairly 5. cruel, vindictive, crude; member of platoon, makes crude jokes about death 6. kind, compassionate, wise; guides O'Brien in decision about draft 7. young, lovely, becomes bloodthirsty; symbolizes what war does to people 8. quiet, introspective; emotional scars from war lead to his suicide 9. efficient, brave; platoon's medic 10. brags, exaggerates; dies horrible death that leaves emotional scars on others **(B)** 11. c (p. 126) 12. b (p. 21) 13. a (p. 61) 14. d (inference) 15. b (throughout) 16. c (pp. 57–59) 17. d (pp. 68–76) 18. a (p. 127) 19. b (p. 156) 20. c (inference) **(C)** 21. thinks he loved Martha more than his men (p. 6) 22. mindless retaliation, frustration with war, grief (pp. 78–79, inference) 23. the death of innocence (pp. 105, 114) 24. because he must have killed someone (p. 131) 25. He thinks it's his fault because he let go of Kiowa's boot (pp. 148–149) 26. tells crude jokes (p. 165) 27. going into the slimy water where Kiowa died and submerging Kiowa's moccasins (pp. 186–188) 28. mess with his mind (p. 201) 29. Charlie Cong (p. 202) 30. He shoots himself in the foot so he can leave Vietnam (pp. 219–223) 31. Linda's death (pp. 227–228) 32. with stories about them (p. 239) 33. his death in the field of mud and human waste; thinks he caused Kiowa's death (pp. 170–171) 34. because he didn't save Kiowa (pp. 141–142) 35. Survive—O'Brien, Bowker, Cross, Azar, Kiley; Die—Lavender, Lemon, Kiowa (p. 245, inference) **(D)** 36. simile (p. 15) 37. metaphor (p. 78) 38. metaphor (p. 80) 39. simile (p. 43) **(E&F)** Responses will vary.